Don't Swing from the Balcony, Romeo

MICHAEL GREEN

Drawings by John Jensen

SPHERE BOOKS LIMITED
London and Sydney

First published in Great Britain by
Secker and Warburg Ltd 1983

Published by Sphere Books Ltd 1984
30–32 Gray's Inn Road, London WC1X 8JL

Printed and bound in Great Britain by
Cox & Wyman Ltd, Reading

FOREWORD

This slim volume has been written because of the warm public response to its even slimmer predecessor *Tonight, Josephine*, the first collection of imaginary letters to and from the famous. However, not all the allusions in *Tonight, Josephine* were recognised. No one except me and the publisher seemed to know that Benjamin Franklin invented the lightning conductor by flying a kite in a thunderstorm with a key attached to the string. Since it is inevitable that at least one letter is going to baffle someone, this time I have provided a key at the back of the book. I hope no one feels insulted by this, but what is obvious to one person is obscure to somebody else. You are on your honour not to look at the key first.

I should like to thank many friends and acquaintances for their suggestions, and also Daphne Burgess of Portsmouth, whose prize-winning entry in the *Books and Bookmen* competition run with *Tonight, Josephine* has been used as a basis for one letter in this volume.

Michael Green
London, 1983

Florence
April 5, 1543

Dear Lady Capulet,

It is just as well you called me in to look at the balcony in Miss Juliet's bedroom because it might have collapsed any minute. The supporting column has been badly weakened. Someone has carved the initial R so deeply as to nearly sever it. Hearts have also been carved all over it and graffiti scratched on the surface, rubbish like, "O, that I were a glove upon that hand that I might touch that cheek," etc., etc. A rope has been fixed to the support and someone has been swinging from it. There are a series of what look like nailmarks on the wall as if a person was trying to claw their way up. It really is disgusting what these vandals get up to today. The trouble is, everyone is too soft with them. They should bring back the rack.

I have repaired the damage as far as possible, removed the rope and plastered over the filthy writing. But it is essential for the cement to harden properly, so the balcony must not be used for the next 24 hours. If anyone stands on it I shall not be answerable for the consequences.

Yours faithfully,

G. Tomasino
Builder and decorator

SHADRAK, MESHAK and ABEDNEGO
Heating Engineers

Babylon
Nov. 8, 606 BC

Dear Friend,

May we draw your attention to a completely new service which we are offering to our valued customers? In the past, routine maintenance of a furnace has meant closing down the whole system. Even the smallest crack in the holocaust meant cutting off the fires and doing without hot water and baths, apart from the added inconvenience of having nowhere to throw political opponents, dissident slaves, etc., etc.

We can now avoid this unfortunate situation. We have evolved a new technique by which we actually service your furnace while it is still operating! Yes, you can even heat it up and put more fuel on while we are working inside it. In a recent test a furnace was heated to three times its normal heat and we were still able to carry on within.

This is a service operated by the three partners in the firm. Why not make use of it this week? An application form is enclosed.

Remember – our new system has been personally tested by us in the presence of His Majesty King Nebuchadnezzar, who expressed himself totally satisfied with the result.

What's good enough for the King should be good enough for you! Don't delay! Apply today!

Yours cordially,

SHADRAK, MESHAK and ABEDNEGO

By Royal Appointment Heating Consultants to
His Majesty King Nebuchadnezzar

Aug 5 885

Mistress

While I was watching ye cakes on ye fire a party of Danes arrived. When I came out of hiding ye cakes were burned.

Also ye house.

And ye village

Alfred

(King)

Oberheist, Switzerland
Feb. 17, 1234

Dear Bro. Bernard,

I would like to discuss with you the situation that has arisen over your dog. I don't want to ban all pets in the monastery but the position is becoming impossible. I appreciate your motives in training the animal to go out into the pass and seek travellers buried in the snow are of the highest, but it is disrupting our work. Five times in the last week all the monks have been called out because your dog got lost. Twice it had to be dug out of snowdrifts and carried back frozen on a stretcher. During this time there have been no human travellers lost at all. Indeed, there *are* no travellers at this time of the year, and the only living thing in the pass is your dog. I understand last time it disappeared you tied a small barrel of brandy round your neck so you could revive it when it was found. Really, this is quite ridiculous. Please see me tomorrow.

Yours

DOM Christopher, Abbot

Hastings
Oct. 13, 1066

Varlet!

Tomorrow I have to meet the dastard William of Normandy in battle and none of my armour fits. It may be strong and well-made but you do not know my size in anything. At the battle of Stamford Bridge last week my chain mail was so long it hung out three inches in front of my toes and once an enemy stuck a spear through it and pinned me to the ground. My gauntlets were so big that when I whirled my two-handed sword round my head they flew off into the distance, taking the sword with them. Now, on the eve of the most important battle I have had to fight, what do I find? My helmet is too small. I cannot even get it on. I need a 7¾ at least and this is only a 6½.

As a result I shall have to fight tomorrow without any protection for my head. I am very worried about this as the Normans have a cunning tactic by which they shoot arrows high into the air so they land in their opponents' ears and they do not hear the order to advance. If I get an arrow in the ear I shall blame you.

Consider yourself dismissed as royal armourer.

King Harold

Pisa
Jan. 11, 1173

Dear Bishop,

I am most upset to hear that the new tower I designed is leaning towards the North. No, I do not recollect you telling me it was not straight during the construction. However, I was extremely sorry to hear about the bellringers who slid out of the windows; also about Bro. Guiseppe, who I gather has not been seen since he went to hoist a flag on the roof a week ago. Yes, I do agree it is awkward kneeling in prayer at a steep angle. I also appreciate the difficulty you mention about drinking soup.

I have made enquiries and I now discover that the tower leans because the builder who excavated the foundations made a simple error and dug out a cellar on one side which should have been on the other. Do not fear. I shall strengthen the foundations of the appropriate side and since the tower will sink slightly in any case, it will eventually settle down level.

I will light a candle for Bro. Guiseppe.

Yours faithfully,

Bonanno Pisano
Architect

Hell
Jan. 10, 1559

Dear Faustus,
I shall call for you next Monday at half-past eleven in the evening. And then back to my place, mmm? Nothing formal, just a little barbecue. Some of the guests may be in tails but you wear what you please.

Yours sincerely,

Lucifer

Altdorf,
Lucerne
April 3, 1467

Dear Mr Tell,

You must give up this madness. Yesterday your son was carried into my surgery on a stretcher with an arrow sticking out of his forehead. This is the third time in a week he has been brought here. Earlier I had to treat him for wounds in the leg and then the chest. Yet your only comment has been, "At least my aim is getting better." Mercifully, your son is now out of danger but he might not be so lucky next time. Also, we had trouble removing the apple from his head. There was surely no need to glue it to his scalp?

Mr Tell, I implore you to desist.

Yours faithfully,

Dr R. Strabismus

Ekron
May 3, 998 BC

My Dear Son,

I want you to be very brave. Your father has been killed fighting those goddamn Israelites. I would like to be able to say he went the way he wanted to go, but I am afraid they killed him with a dirty trick. Your father was a big, big man and afraid of nobody. No one in the Israelite army could match him. So when he challenged them to single combat on behalf of us Philistines they sent out, not their biggest man, but a little shepherd boy called David. Well, your father always did like kids so he bent down to pat him on the head. And as he did so the evil little brat threw a stone at him from only three feet away. It hit him on the temple and he died instantly. Then do you know what the sadistic little bastard did? He borrowed a sword and cut off your father's head.

Those Israelites are always up to some cheat or other. Look what they did to Jericho. It may take years to repair those walls.

I want you to be a good boy and say your prayers to Baal every night like your father taught you. I am sending you his sword to keep separately. It may take some time to arrive as it needs six men to carry it.

Your loving mother

Greenwich Palace
Oct. 4, 1593

Dear Cecil,

Pray send for my physician. I have hurt my leg and may have a fever. While disembarking from the Royal Barge at Greenwich today I was about to step round a suspicious-looking piece of boggy ground when that fool Sir Walter Raleigh throws his cloak on top of the mire and implores me to tread on it. Not wishing to appear ungrateful in front of such a large crowd I did so. I immediately sank up to my waist in a disused sump which stank of heaven knows what and had to be rescued by a rope. The only consolation is that Raleigh's expensive purple cloak is ruined. I personally trod it deep down into the filth and refused to let anyone salvage it.

Of course Raleigh grovelled and swore it was an accident. He said that if I would only forgive him he would go and colonise somewhere and name it after me. Kindly see that he does so, preferably not in America again.

Elizabeth R

Drury Lane,
London
March 17, 1806

Dear Mr Grimaldi,

Thank you for letting us see your act. To be quite frank, we did not think it very funny. Was it deliberate when your trousers caught fire? Your make-up was rather grotesque, too, all white-faced and red-lipped. In these days of lighting by the new oxy-hydrogen gas, stage make-up can be more subtle.

Your last trick, when you stood on your head on a horse and played "Rule Britannia" on two trumpets while kicking a ball from one foot to the other is, I am afraid, the sort of old-fashioned stuff that doesn't appeal these days. People tend to want something spectacular now. Are you any good at imitating Napoleon?

Once again, thank you for calling. Don't write to us, we'll write to you.

Yours sincerely,

A. Stephens, Manager

Troy
June 8, 1193 BC

Dear Helen,

I think it was rather unwise of you to launch 1,000 ships simultaneously yesterday. The harbour is completely blocked. I'm afraid it's made you very unpopular with the authorities. The harbourmaster asked me to tell you not to show your face around here again.

Love

Menelaus

On Board HMS *Bounty*
March 5, 1789

Dear Mr Christian,

I am herewith giving you written warning about your conduct, which is in serious breach of the Articles of War and Admiralty rules.

I think you know to what I am referring, namely your habit of smoking the tobacco on duty. Last week you set the mainsail alight when a spark from your pipe fell on it during reefing. You had no business to be smoking in the rigging. Worse still, when I made an inspection I found you had nailed an ashtray to the mast. It was full.

When the binnacle was checked last Tuesday the bosun reported that it was clogged up with ash and scrapings from your pipe. No wonder the compass kept pointing East. I can understand now why you are always so keen to check the course. I suppose this is your way of retaliating for the fact that I will not provide ashtrays on the quarter-deck.

I need scarcely remind you of the seriousness of your latest misdemeanour, when you knocked out your pipe on a cannon yesterday and it went off. It is a miracle no one was hurt. Heaven knows what would happen if your duties ever took you into the powder magazine. As it is, I have had to appoint a seaman to follow you around with a bucket of water, but we are short-handed and cannot spare men for this all the time.

You have been warned time after time about your conduct but you pay no attention. The First Lieutenant has just reported that you asked the Admiral for a light when he came on board. This is mutiny, Mr Christian.

J. Bligh, Captain

Poldu,
Cornwall
July 31, 1901

Dear Mr Marconi,

What went wrong? We waited twelve hours here in Cornwall for your signal from across the Atlantic but no telegram came through. I always said it wouldn't work without wires.

Yours sincerely,

A. Wrench
Chief Engineer

Brook Street,
London W.
Jan. 4, 1891

Dear Sir,

I am sorry to say the portrait which you painted of me is completely unsatisfactory. Not only does it make me look much older than I am, but there appears to be a bloodstain on one of the hands. The eyes are bloodshot and bleary and the face looks diseased. There is a nasty snarl on the lips. I regret I must ask you to return the 100 guineas I paid.

Yours faithfully,

J. Dorian Gray

Mon Repos,
Ulan Bator,
Mongolia
July 3, 1218

Dear Genghis,

Your mother and I are very worried about you. We do not like the sort of people you are mixing with. Believe me, those Kurds never were any good. They have the highest unemployment-rate of anyone in Asia.

We also hear alarming reports of what you are doing. We are afraid you are giving way to your tantrums again, as you did when a little boy. I do hope you have not started grinding your teeth again. We thought we had cured you of that by hitting you on the head every time you did it.

Mrs Oktu next door says someone told her you have just laid waste to Central Asia. We feel so ashamed we dare not show our faces. Have we failed you in some way? Your mother and I always did our best. Maybe we ought to have been stricter but after you bit off your mother's little finger, we didn't like to be too stern.

Is it too late to suggest you settle down and get a respectable job as a herdsman? We do not like the thought of our little boy living on mares' milk and fried dung with those awful people. You always used to like a good feed even if you had to strangle the animal yourself.

Please come home. Your little room is just as you left it, right down to your sister's skull on the dressing-table.

Your loving father

Somewhere in Fife
Oct. 5, 1306

Dear Jock,

I cannot tell you of the horrors I have experienced since the English crushed us. I have been harried across the countryside and forced to take refuge in caves and holes in the ground. My present abode is the worst so far. It is a damp cave, not more than eight feet deep and the same in height, and, horror of horrors, it is covered in spiders. As you know, I can't stand them. I have an obsession they will scuttle up my kilt. I spend most of my time cringing in a corner to avoid them or trying to kill some with my sword. However, even in adversity we can learn something. I think this plague of spiders is sent to tell me something. Well, I shall heed the lesson. It is no use trying again. My motto in future will be, "If at first you don't succeed, quit." I shall give up and go home.

Yours aye,

Robert Bruce

Salzburg,
Austria
Sept. 4, 1194

To Leopold, Duke of Austria
From Richard Coeur-de-Lion, of England

Sire,

Is it not enough to have captured me on returning from the Crusade to the Holy Land and to have imprisoned me here without any communication with my realm of England, without your adding to my torment? Every day I am tortured almost beyond endurance by a minstrel who appears outside the window of my cell and keeps singing the same song, one I helped compose many years ago in London. He is too far away to identify but I can only suppose this man is employed by yourself as a further instrument of misery for me. It is torment to have to listen to the same song day after day, repeated again and again, until the refrain goes through my head like a hammer. I have attempted to drive the minstrel away by throwing things through the bars of the window but he only approaches nearer and now he has taken to grimacing and winking at me. He keeps pointing to himself and yesterday he held up a large placard with the words

TELL ME HOW MUCH THE RANSOM IS

written on it. A cruel jest to one who has no hope of ransom, since nobody knows where I am. Please order the man to go away. If you will not do that, in God's name let him sing another song.

Richard

Alexandria
July 8, 45 BC

No dear, you should have used *asses'* milk, not *asps'*. No wonder you had difficulty getting enough to fill a bath. Asps are for committing suicide with.

Cleopatra

The Palace,
Ur,
Chaldea
570 BC

To the Chamberlain:

Something has got to be done about the state of the palace. For some time it has been getting dirtier and dirtier. Now the walls are covered in graffiti. Only last night I was holding a feast – nothing expensive, just a few sucking pigs and concubines – when to my horror I discovered someone had actually scrawled on the wall behind me

MENE, MENE, TEKEL, UPHARSIN

There was no clue as to who had done it, except for a large hand-print.

To make it worse, I don't even know what it means. Some kids' gibberish, I suppose. Please have it removed and see that nobody else is allowed to write all over the palace walls. It makes one wonder what will happen next.

BELSHAZZAR

MENE MENE
TEKEL
UPHARSIN

The Verger's Cottage,
Stoke Poges,
Buckinghamshire
July 27, 1750

Dear Rector,

The Scribbling Gentleman has been here again. He keeps wandering around the churchyard muttering to himself and talking gibberish and writing in a notebook. Yesterday I found him staring at a grave and saying, "Each in his narrow cell for ever laid, the rude forefathers of the hamlet sleep." I told him there was no need to call my father rude or anyone else's for that matter. He peered at me in a strange fashion and then asked, "Are you some mute inglorious Milton? Or perhaps some village Hampden that with dauntless breast the petty tyrant of the field withstood?" I told him to keep a civil tongue in his head. It is well-known that Half-Witted Jack is the village Hampden. I am a married man myself.

Later he quarrelled with John Molesworthy, who had just been ploughing fifteen-acre. "Ah, my good fellow," he said, "I perceive the lowing herd is winding slowly over the lea."

"Indeed they are, your reverence," said John, "and that is because you have left the bloody gate open. I shall have to go and fetch 'em back and stop 'em winding."

"Then," said the Scribbling Gentleman, "you will doubtless homeward plod your weary way."

"No, I shall not," replied John. "I shall run to Widow Johnson's so as to have half an hour with her before her lodger comes home."

I also fear the Scribbling Gentleman may be unduly attracted towards the fair sex. He keeps muttering about "storied urn and animated bust".

In the end I could tolerate his behaviour no longer. I

pointed to him the way out of the churchyard. "There is your path home, sir," I told him. He replied, "The paths of glory lead but to the grave." "No, sir," I said, "the graves are the other way." He merely laughed at me and went off.

I wish your reverence would return and deal with him.

Your obedient servant

Amos Jacob, verger

At Sea off Copenhagen
April 3, 1801

To the Admiral Commanding,
Portsmouth Dockyard,
Hampshire,
England.

Sir,

I wish to protest in the strongest terms about the telescopes which the Victualling and Supply Division have been issuing to the Baltic Fleet. Yesterday, while cruising off Copenhagen, I was ordered by Admiral Sir Hyde Parker, my commanding officer, to withdraw in the face of an enemy fleet. On placing a telescope to my good eye, however, I could see no ships. Indeed I could hardly see anything at all, just a blur. I therefore inadvertently sailed straight into the enemy, totally against orders. It is fortunate I was able to destroy them or I should be facing a court-martial for disobedience.

On examining the defective telescope it was discovered that it was designed to be used with the right eye. It is well known I have a patch over that eye, which I lost in the Mediterranean, so the instrument was quite useless to me. All the telescopes are the same so I am unable to pick out anything at a distance.

Please have the goodness to send a supply of new telescopes immediately. There is no telling what trouble I shall get into until they arrive.

I have the honour to be sir,
Your obedient servant

Horatio Nelson

Whitechapel
Jan. 17, 1901

Dear Professor Higgins,

Thank you for all the trouble you have taken. But after only one lesson I find I can speak English like what a perfect lady can, so I have gone back to my old room in the East End.

Remember me to Colonel Pickering,

Yours sincerely,

Eliza Doolittle

Trinity College,
Cambridge
Sept. 4, 1685

Wife,

Be so good as to have the garden hammock placed under another tree. Let the gardener see to it at once. Today I was lying in the hammock trying to work out a difficult mathematical formula concerned with gravitation when an apple fell on my head and drove all thoughts of it from my mind.

Isaac

Pisa
Feb. 12, 1178

Dear Bishop,

It was a great blow to me to hear the tower now leans to the South, especially after all the trouble we took digging the foundations out. Are you sure it isn't just the wind? Or perhaps you should rehang the bells, with the heavier ones the other side?

Yes, I do appreciate that you have now lost six monks since Bro. Guiseppe and now no one will go up to take down the flag. I shall light candles for them. As regards the difficulty in praying, when everyone slid to the wall as they kneeled, might I suggest everyone faces at right angles to the slope?

I really was hoping not to have to bother with this problem again, as I am very busy working on the Renaissance just now. I think the trouble can be rectified once and for all by digging out the foundations on one side.

Yours faithfully,

Bonanno Pisano
Architect

Field Headquarters
Army of the Marne
August 30, 1914

Mon Commandant,
My centre is giving way, my right is in retreat. Situation disastrous. I shall retire.

Marshal Foch

PLYMOUTH BOWLS CLUB

Plymouth Hoe,
Devon
June 5, 1588

Dear Sir Francis Drake,

The Committee have asked me to inform you that your membership is to be terminated forthwith for misconduct. It is one of the strictest rules of the club that members must not occupy the green after their allotted period has expired. As you know, playing space is too small for our large membership. Yesterday, when it was pointed out that you were already a quarter of an hour over your finishing time and another group were waiting to play, you replied, "We have still time to finish our game of bowls," and insisted upon doing so, taking another half an hour.

Your explanation afterwards that you thought someone said, "The Armada is coming," and you wished to set an example of calmness is deemed unsatisfactory. In fact, when you had won your game you immediately ran down to the harbour shouting, "Where the hell are those ---- Spaniards?"

Please note that you also owe a year's subscription. And kindly do not pay it in Spanish doubloons this time. We can't get them changed anywhere.

I am, Sir,

Your obedient Servant,

R. Trelawney (General Secretary)

Eastcheap,
London
Oct. 8, 1479

To the Keeper of the Tower of London

Sir,

I am sending back the last butt of malmsey you sold me from the Tower surplus. Every one of my customers has complained about the taste. What on earth have you put in it?

Yours faithfully,

A. Goodman, wine merchant

Gizeh,
Cairo
Jan. 30,
2900 BC

To King Cheops of Egypt

Your Majesty,

O King, live for ever and be not angry when I report that the monument you caused to be erected here at Gizeh has not been built exactly as you instructed. Your Awfulness required a prone figure, like a lion, with a human face of imposing majesty and power. All has been accomplished in the incredibly short space of seven years, though not without much trial and tribulation. After the plague of locusts so much overtime had to be worked we ran out of whips. At last, however, all is complete and satisfactory but for one detail. I fear that the expression on the face of The Great Sphinx will not please your Frightfulness. It has an enigmatic smile.

This is due to an error by the chief stonemason who was working on the lips. He held his section of the plan upside down unfortunately, so instead of the corners of the mouth drooping in ferocity, they go up, giving the impression of a faint, but quite perceptible, condescending smirk, not the fearsome expression you intended. We tried to correct it by altering the corners of the mouth but this only made matters worse and we had to stop as the mouth was getting wider and wider and beginning to look like a hideous grin. Unfortunately the architect was not there to supervise as you had him buried alive after he'd finished the Great Pyramid next door. I tried knocking for two days on the outside but received no reply.

Since I have no wish to share a similar fate I am writing this on a fast chariot heading North.

May Thy Shadow Never Grow Less,

Your obedient servant

Chnemtops the Naramite (contractor)

US Army Headquarters,
Hawaii
April 10, 1942

Mr President,

Yesterday Japanese troops finally occupied Bataan. This is to let you know I have no intention of returning. I never did like the place anyway and my wife hated it. The climate stank and the flies were awful. Even the officers' club was lousy. The Japs can't make the place worse and they might even improve it. I am very glad they conquered the goddamn swamp and I hope they all get malaria, like we did.

Yours sincerely,

General J. MacArthur

Rome
554 BC

Dear Spurius and Herminius,

You rotten bastards. You filthy, evil, treacherous, cowardly swine. What the hell do you mean by abandoning me at the bridge after that fracas with Lars Porsena the other day?

All right, I admit you helped me to hold the bridge, although I must remind you I was the only one to get wounded, receiving a nasty cut on the thigh from Astur, Lord of Luna. But when the City Fathers had chopped down the bridge and cried, "Come back, come back, Horatius," you two knocked me over in the rush to get across before it finally collapsed. As an English poet named Macaulay, who happened to be present, phrased it:

> Back darted Spurius Lartius;
> Herminius darted back;
> And as they passed, beneath their feet
> They felt the timbers crack.
>
> Alone stood brave Horatius
> But constant still in mind;
> Thrice thirty thousand foes before
> And the broad flood behind.

My only criticism of that verse is the word "darted". I would have substituted "fled shrieking with terror". At any rate, it sums up the predicament you left me in nicely. Nearly 100,000 gibbering enemies in front of me, with Sextus and Lars Porsena leering in triumph, and you two safely across the bridge and the flooded Tiber my only way of escape. It is lucky I am a strong swimmer. Not many could have swum across in full armour while bleeding to death. Next time you two can hold the bridge by yourselves while I shout advice from the farther shore.

Yours,

Horatius

PRESERVED BY MIRACLE WHEN YACHT
SANK STOP SAVED BY GOOD SHIP
TITANIC STOP ARRIVE NEW YORK
TOMORROW STOP WEATHER COLD
OTHERWISE ALL WELL STOP PETE

Pisa
April 2, 1201

Dear Bishop,

I have taken over from my employer, the late Bonanno Pisano, who has recently committed suicide by jumping from your tower. I see from his records that at the time of his death he had made fourteen alterations to the tower, digging out the foundations to the North seven times and to the South seven times. From your latest letter I gather the tower still refuses to remain upright.

I have given a lot of thought to the matter and examined the structure. In my opinion it is now totally unsafe, as it is built on ground liable to subsidence. I therefore recommend that you do nothing as it will probably fall down within a few years. We can then plan a new tower, worthy of the city of Pisa, which will last for centuries, long after the old tower has been forgotten.

Yours

G. Arturo
Architect

Elsinore,
Thursday

Dear Sexton,

I wish to complain in the strongest possible fashion about your grave-diggers. The other day I had to attend the burial of my sister Ophelia. You may imagine my feelings when, on the procession reaching the grave, we found the chief grave-digger and his assistant standing in it singing, exchanging jokes and roaring with laughter. They were also speaking disrespectfully to the Prince Hamlet.

Worst of all, however, is the fact that they were throwing human remains around. The senior grave-digger actually tossed a skull in the air and began to talk to it. He identified the skull as belonging to Thos. Yorick, the late court jester. Unfortunately, a relative of the aforesaid Yorick was nearby trying to put some flowers on his grave and was naturally distressed. He told me afterwards he did not know where to put the flowers as the grave-diggers had scattered his father all over the cemetery.

Furthermore, the grave that they were digging for the Lady Ophelia was too small, so she had to be buried standing up. I must explain that this was why I jumped into the grave – to try and enlarge it. Unfortunately, Prince Hamlet took exception to certain remarks of mine and jumped in too and tried to strangle me, so I was unable to carry out my task.

Things have gone from bad to worse since my father Polonius died, but you must try to keep up standards. For a start I suggest you sack the No. 1 grave-digger, the one who's always making those unfunny puns. Some of his jokes are so bad he deserves sacking for that alone.

You must also arrange for Mr Yorick to be reburied in a decent manner. You will find his skull under the tree about six feet from the Lady Ophelia's grave. I don't know where the rest of him is.

Yours faithfully,

Laertes

221b, Baker Street,
Marylebone,
London.
Dec. 5, 1905

My Dear Holmes,

You will doubtless be surprised to find this letter on your return home this evening but I have decided to leave our chambers in Baker Street and settle in France. The truth is, Holmes, that to the world we have appeared for many years as inseparable companions, the Great Detective with his faithful biographer Dr Watson hovering one pace behind. In reality, the story is less pleasant. Over the past few years I have cherished a deep and growing loathing of you and our life together.

I could put up with the domestic disturbance caused by your work, such as the time Professor Moriarty set fire to the flat. This was part of sharing one's existence with a crime investigator. What became unbearable were your filthy habits. It is not particularly pleasant living with a drug addict. Your practice of injecting yourself three times a day with a seven per cent solution of cocaine was bad enough, but what I could not endure was the habit of using the same hypodermic to extract pickled onions from the jar on our supper table. As a result I nearly became an addict myself. That, of course, was assuming you condescended to turn up for supper. I once waited three days for you to arrive for a meal and when you did you were disguised as an elderly cabman.

Neither is it pleasant to share rooms with someone who practises revolver-shooting against the wall (you always were a terrible shot). Or somebody who does chemistry experiments on the dining-table. We both know how near to death I came through eating a piece of cheese on which you had spilled strychnine. Not to mention your habit of playing the violin throughout the night while solving a case. I used to pray for Moriarty to get you. To make it worse you knew only one tune – *The Blue Danube*.

There is another matter; your lack of interest in women, except for your admiration of Irene Adler. I am not a prudish man, Holmes, but by George, if I thought I had been sharing digs with a sodomite I should have you horsewhipped.

Worst of all, Holmes, is the fact that you are an incompetent coward and an impostor.

You constantly criticised my account of your cases in the *Strand Magazine*, yet I gave you credit you did not deserve. The public would never guess from my story *The Speckled Band*, that when the snake came down the bell-rope to claim its victim, you grovelled on the floor screaming, "I can't stand snakes! I'm afraid of them! For God's sake kill it, Watson!" I did so with my walking-stick while you cringed against the wall. And what happened in *The Hound of the Baskervilles*? When that devilish beast leaped at us you fired twelve revolver shots and missed each time, largely because you were trembling so much you couldn't shoot straight. It was I who had to kill it with my old Army pistol. I always used to wonder why you courteously stood aside to let me through the door first when we left the flat, until I discovered Moriarty had got a sniper posted in the house opposite and I was being used as a shield.

But you always treated me as a complete idiot. You said a thousand times in that patronising voice, "You know my methods, Watson." Of course I didn't, nobody did, they were based on guesswork. No one would think I saved your life six times and solved five of your biggest cases.

I am not only leaving you, Holmes, but taking my revenge. (At this I can see you finger the revolver in the pocket of your dressing-gown at the thought of poor simple Watson getting his revenge on someone as clever as you!) The fact is, though, I have a small knowledge of chemistry from my medical training and I have profited from your own researches, mostly conducted while I was trying to eat breakfast. You may remember the Case of the Missing Guitarist, where the murderer killed his victim by coating the strings of his guitar with a secret poison which was absorbed through the skin. You left the formula in the butter dish one morning and I copied it. (That was the case in which you sneered at me because I could not identify a man in Baker Street as a left-handed violinist with a bad-tempered wife.)

It only remains to say, my dear Holmes, that this letter is coated with poison and if you have read this far you must have absorbed sufficient to kill you. As you know, there is no antidote and in any case I doubt if you would have time to reach it. Do not bother to ring for the excellent Mrs Hudson. She has eloped with me to Paris and in two days' time will become the second Mrs Watson. She had become as tired of you as I had. We shall spend our honeymoon at the Reichenbach Falls.

I imagine you will find some comfort in the fact that even the stupid Inspector Lestrade, of Scotland Yard, can hardly fail to deduce a clue from this letter clutched in your hand, and justice must speedily follow. Alas, I have to disappoint you again. Not only is the letter coated in poison but it has also been soaked in a chemical which will cause it to dissolve into ashes within a short time of being taken from the envelope and exposed to air. The only clue to your death, Holmes, will be a pile of grey ash in your hand. A nice riddle for the Great Detective to solve and one you would have rejoiced over. Unfortunately, Inspector Lestrade lacks your extensive knowledge of scientific research and will doubtless dismiss the ash (which you would have identified at once) as something of no importance.

Goodbye, my dear fellow. I shall convey my condolences to your brother Mycroft.

Your old friend and colleague,

John H. Watson, MD

The Assembly,
Paris
March 30, 1793

Dear Madame Defarge,

Thank you so much for the gifts of knitting. I need not tell you how useful they will be for the gift stall in aid of former prisoners in the Bastille. Don't worry about the stains – the blood came off quite easily. We now have 200 Phrygian caps, which I think is enough for the present. Perhaps you could now concentrate on something slightly different. Scarves in the revolutionary colours of red, white and blue would be nice.

I was sorry to hear about your husband's fingers. Of course, when operating the guillotine, it is essential to stand well clear.

Yours sincerely,

P. Robespierre (Citizen)

Big Sea Water,
Illinois
March 4, 1881

To the Railroad Superintendent

Sir,

Recently I bought a ticket
Took the money to the office
Gave it to the balding paleface
Sitting in the ticket office.
In his skinny hand he clutched it
While the oil lamp flared around him
Like the moon on Gitche Gumee
And he gave to me a ticket,
It was valid for Chicago.
Yes, Chicago said the ticket
It would take me to Chicago.
Not to Denver, Colorado,
It would take me to Chicago.
I paid dollars for the ticket,
Dollars that had got a face on
Like the face of some great chieftain
Wise and smiling in his wisdom,
So my dollars for the ticket.

When the moon had lit the pine trees,
Lit the pine trees with her fragrance
Not the oak trees with her fragrance
But the pine trees lit she brightly,
Came the eastbound locomotive,
Stopped exactly at the depot
Stopped precisely where it ought to.
And I got into the coaches
Coaches labelled for Chicago
These the coaches I got into
Like some bright and shining wigwams

On the shores of Big Sea Water.
Soon I fell into a slumber
Fell into a mighty slumber
Snored into the air like thunder
Three hours snored my mighty bellows
Then awoke with sudden shivering
And a mouth like bison droppings.

When I asked, "Is this Chicago?"
I was greeted with loud laughter
And they said the locomotive
Had a coupling rod that fractured,
As they tried to leave the depot
So the coupling rod it fractured.
And I waited till the morning
But we never left the depot
Where the coupling rod was fractured.
So I'm writing you this letter
Asking you to pay the money
For the ticket to Chicago
Not to Denver, Colorado
But the ticket to Chicago.
Fourteen dollars and a nickel
This I paid to reach Chicago
And I never left the depot.
Send the money by Wells Fargo.

Yours faithfully,

A. Hiawatha (Chief)

...ouch!

Camelot,
Tuesday

Dear Arthur,

Just a line from your ever-loving wife to wish you every success against the dragon tomorrow and against Sir Mordred on Thursday. I know you are terribly busy, darling, but could I ask a small favour? When you come into my bedroom to make love could you take your armour off next time? Last week you didn't even have time to take off your helmet. The bit which falls down at the front slipped and cut my nose while you were kissing me although you didn't notice as you had problems of your own with your chain-mail trousers at the time. Incidentally, there is a hole in the right leg of your chain-mail. When you come back I will darn it for you with a piece of wire if you will put the trousers out.

I was very upset to hear that bloody fool Sir Bedivere had thrown your sword Excalibur into the lake again. Why does he keep doing this? I gather from Lancelot that he almost hit a swimmer, who just managed to stick out his arm and grasp the hilt. It must be very tiring having to drag the lake every time. Why don't you throw Sir Bedivere in the water instead?

A small toad has just hopped into the room. It is Merlin again, under the pathetic impression nobody recognises him. I will ask him to do something about Sir Bedivere's obsession with the lake.

Your loving wife

Guinevere

Xanadu
September 5, 1260

His Imperial Nobleness Kubla Khan

Your Majesty,

Following your instructions we have completed a full survey of the site as specified.

We found subterranean water in vast quantities which could lead to rising damp and other structural difficulties, especially in conjunction with an underground cave system which extends so far in all directions it was impossible to secure accurate measurements. This could lead to subsidence.

In addition we are informed that the area is zoned as one of outstanding natural beauty and planning permission for a pleasure dome is unlikely to be granted.

We therefore recommend that your Majesty does not proceed with the project at Xanadu.

Yours faithfully,

Vandal, Mongol and Goth
Chartered Surveyors

New Plymouth,
Cape Cod
March 3, 1621

Dear Father O'Flannagan,

I am afraid I cannot agree to return you to England for nothing. I appreciate you got on board *The Mayflower* in Plymouth by mistake, thinking it was going to Ireland, but I am not to blame if you didn't discover your mistake for two weeks because you were drunk all the time. I sympathise over the unpleasant trip but it was your own fault for trying to get the pilgrims to pray to the Blessed St Francis and cross themselves. After all, they *are* Puritans. Why not concentrate on converting the Indians? They will do anything for a few beads.

Capt. Jones
Master, *The Mayflower*

St Peter's,
Rome
June 10, 1511

Dear Signor Michelangelo,

I cannot tell you with what horror I have just seen the work you have been doing in the Sistine Chapel. When we said we wanted you to paint the ceiling, we meant whitewashed, not covered in pictures. You were distinctly asked to decorate the walls with murals, not the ceiling. How is anyone going to see the pictures you have painted up there? They will have to lie on their backs to do so. The architect was going to put a skylight in the roof but I don't see how he can do so now, since it will make a hole in one of the cherubs in an awkward place.

One of the bishops has also raised an interesting point. Isn't there a danger that the paint could drop off the ceiling? The whole complicated painting could easily fall to the floor in one solid piece. Or bits might flake off on to people worshipping below. I do not wish to celebrate Mass amid a rain of debris.

Meanwhile the walls are still bare. I really do despair. You can't have the simplest things done these days without having to supervise it yourself. Please come and discuss it at once. Perhaps it isn't too late to have the whole thing painted over.

Yours faithfully,

Julius II (Pope)

Uz,
Thursday

Dear Job,

Sorry to find you in such low spirits when I called the other day with Eliphaz and Bildad. It was a miracle we found you at all. As you know, we called at your house only to find it had been burnt down. What were all those bodies in the ruins? One of them looked like your wife.

Now as a friend I am going to speak plainly to you. Eliphaz, Bildad and I feel you have given way to self-pity. I appreciate that all your oxen and sheep and goats have been carried away and all your servants put to the sword and all your sons and daughters killed when their house collapsed during a feast; but you are not the only one with troubles in this world. Only the other day my chariot wheel fell off and I just can't get it repaired. People don't seem to want small jobs these days.

We believe you should pull yourself together. The first step must be to smarten yourself up. No wonder you are so depressed if you go around in sackcloth all the time, especially when your robe is covered in ashes. I don't think you should spend all your time sitting by the fire crying, "Woe is me," and throwing ashes all over your head. Take up some hobby that will lift you out of yourself. And do something about your personal appearance. Your complexion is a disgrace, all covered in boils. It is no use scraping them with a potsherd, that is an old remedy. You must eat plenty of fruit and bathe them in hot water night and day. A clean body is a cheerful mind.

Try to pull yourself together and think positively. Try to see the funny side of life. Don't take things too seriously. I want you to promise you will make a joke every day and greet each morning with a smile.

Eliphaz, Bildad and myself think part of the trouble is that you are too impatient. You want everything to come right all at once. Just remember we all have to go sometime and if it's your turn today it's ours tomorrow (although perhaps not mine – I feel special arrangements may be made in my case).

I have to close now as I think there is a whirlwind coming.

Remember – think *good* thoughts.

Your old friend

Zophar (the Naamanite)

P.S. *All* your sons and daughters dead? Gee, that's tough. But glad to hear your wife was spared. You see, there's always a silver lining.

...AND NOW I'M PLAGUED BY SOCIAL WORKERS !

University of London
June 30, 1928

Dear Fletcher,

You really are neglecting your job as laboratory assistant. I left out some dishes containing cultures over the weekend and when I returned this morning they were covered in a green mould which had destroyed the germs I was trying to cultivate. Please see the dishes are cleaned out and sterilised and the mould destroyed in case it does some more damage.

Yours

Alexander Fleming

Bristol
April 5, 1773

I am returning the parrot. It keeps saying, "Pieces of nine."

J. Silver

Portsmouth
July 19, 1545

Vice Admiral Sir George Carew
On Board *Mary Rose*
Lying at Portsmouth

Sir,

I beseech you for Godde's sake not to sail today until you have examined ye shippe. For my master carpenter comes running to me this morn and informs me one of ye forgetful knaves who repaired ye vessel hath confessed he did omit to put back ye draine plugge in ye bottom of ye shippe. His wyfe hath just found it in ye pocket of his doublet. Thus ye vessel is slowly filling with water even as you read this letter, which I send by ye fastest rider and ye swiftest horse that I can, yet I still fear I shall be too late and all will miscarry. Godde grant it doth not and that ye Kinge be spared ye awful sight of his most noble bark *Mary Rose* foundering in front of his eyes off Southsea Castle.

I am sending ye draine plugge with ye messenger who carrieth this letter. It goeth in near ye sterne by ye rudder pintle right at ye bottome of ye shippe, but for Godde's sake hurry, my master.

Jacob Holdfast
Master shipwright

Donken School,
Amsterdam
Feb. 19, 1883

Dear Mrs Tromp,

I have sent your son Jan home early from school with this note as he has been very naughty. During the recent floods, when one of the dykes threatened to give way under the pressure of water, some holes were bored in it to give relief. I am sorry to say that today Jan put his thumb in one of the holes and refused to remove it. He was, of course, endangering the whole city by his action. I have called the entire school together and warned them of the danger of putting their thumbs into holes in dykes. What would happen if everyone went around doing this? The whole of Holland would be under water.

Yours sincerely

Mynheer Jacob Van Dusel
Headmaster

From the Mayor's Office,
City Hall,
Sodom
(Twinned with Gomorrah)
August 3rd, 4,356 BC

To the Town Clerk:

I think we should do something about that pillar of salt that has appeared outside the city walls. Could it be turned into a fountain, for instance? Or perhaps people could tie camels to it. We shall also have to do something about that strange man who keeps guarding it. He is obviously mad. When I was up there the other day he pointed to the pillar and said, "I want you to meet the wife." On Mother's Day he put some flowers on it.

Maybe this is something we should discuss with the people at Gomorrah. After all, we have a lot in common.

The Mayor

15
shekels
the
LOT!
SALT

Canal Street,
Birmingham
March 10, 1882

Dear Sir,

I see in the *Manufacturer's Gazette* you have perfected a way of making silk purses out of sows' ears. Allow me to congratulate you on inventing a process that has baffled the civilised world for centuries. It so happens I have just successfully introduced a process for making sows' ears from silk purses, after much experiment. Perhaps we could collaborate to our mutual advantage?

Yours faithfully

J. Smith

Junction Road,
Manchester
March 14, 1882

Dear Sir,

Many thanks for your letter *re* sows' ears. I am glad you wrote as there is a shortage of the natural product. Sows' ears are almost unobtainable in this part of the world. We are willing to take all your output.

Yours faithfully

A. Jones

Canal Street,
Birmingham
March 18, 1882

Dear Sir,

I was very pleased to hear you are willing to take all my output of sows' ears. I shall be very happy to arrange for this. However, there is also a shortage of silk purses in Birmingham at the present time. Could you agree to supply me with all your output of silk purses for manufacture into sows' ears?

Yours faithfully

J. Smith

Junction Road,
Manchester
May 16, 1882

Dear Sir,

This is to inform you we are compelled to increase the cost of our silk purses as supplied to you by ten per cent.

Yours faithfully

A. Jones

Canal Street,
Birmingham
June 14, 1882

Dear Sir,
I regret we shall have to increase the cost of best sows' ears as supplied to you by twenty per cent owing to a rise in the cost of raw materials used in their manufacture.

Yours faithfully

J. Smith

Junction Road,
Manchester
July 15, 1882

Dear Sir,
Just to inform you we have to increase the cost of our silk purses by thirty per cent owing to a rise in the cost of raw materials supplied to us.

Yours faithfully

A. Jones

Canal Street,
Birmingham
August 16, 1882

Dear Sir,
In future the price of best sows' ears will be increased by forty per cent.

Yours faithfully

J. Smith

Junction Road,
Manchester
Sept. 14, 1882

Dear Sir,
This is to inform you we shall cease trading as from the end of the month. Rising prices have forced us out of business.

Yours faithfully

A. Jones

Canal Street,
Birmingham
Sept. 14, 1882

Dear Sir,
I shall be unable to supply you with any more best sows' ears in future as I have gone bankrupt.

Yours faithfully

J. Smith

Blackfriars,
London
Jan. 4, 1672

Dear Andrew Marvell,

This was a filthy trick to publish that disgusting poem dedicated to me because I would not co-operate with your lustful middle-aged desires. You say in the poem, "But at my back I always hear, Time's wingèd chariot hurrying near." Permit me to say in your case it's not merely hovering near, it's standing outside the front door blowing its horn. Some of us however, feel we have a little longer to live and don't have an all-consuming desire to jump into bed with people because we might die at any minute. Yes, I know you get those stabbing pains in your chest. They are much more likely to be due to eating pickled herrings all night with Thos. Kyd and Bob Herrick than your heart.

This wretched verse of yours has ruined me. John Vanbrugh was going to put me in a play until he heard of it. I might even have been presented to the King. The only consolation is that like all your rubbishy poetry, no one will ever read it.

You say, "The grave's a fine and private place." I agree. Drop dead.

Your Coy Mistress

Nashville,
Tennessee
April 19, 1830

Dear brother,

I have made a rare discovery that could make us rich. Up in the hills I have found an animal shaped like a hat. It is a little furry creature and once flayed it needs no further preparation as it just goes straight on to the head with the tail hanging down behind. I have shot one for my own use and made a hat from it, but there must be many more further up in the mountains.

Meanwhile I pledge you to secrecy. If I can find enough of these little creatures I shall make my fortune.

Yours

Davy

Hamelin
March 5, 1487

Dear Heinrich,

Can I ask your advice about a serious problem we have here? The town is plagued with pipers. This morning I counted no fewer than 500 in the main square, all playing in different keys. The noise was frightful. It is estimated there are two thousand altogether in the town. It is the cold weather which drives them here for warmth. Also we have no children (except for a single lame child) so there is nobody to tease and poke fun at them, as happens elsewhere. I am going to offer a reward of ten thousand guilders for the first person to rid the town of them. There are so many, we dare not throw them out.

Sincerely,

A. Schultz
Mayor

Gaul
Ides of March, 55 BC

Dear Pompey,

You will be sorry to hear I have given up the idea of colonising Albion. We sailed across last week on a scouting expedition and had a terrible time. The climate was quite repulsive. It rained continually and everybody got a strange Albion disease they call a "cold". The island is damp, marshy and miserable and there isn't a pine tree in the place. In fact we were greeted by a deputation of local inhabitants led by their Queen Boadicea begging us either to stay or to take them away to a better country. They were sneezing, shivering and short of food and said they were tired of living in such a terrible place. Queen Boadicea became quite nasty when we wouldn't take them away. She even offered to sleep with me if I'd give them a passage to Gaul, but as she looks like the back end of a chariot, I declined. We gave them some wine, which they had never tasted before, and they went wild with joy. They showed us all they have to drink, a filthy concoction of honey. For food they live on boiled cabbage.

I was forced to leave in any case, as the men were threatening to mutiny at having to stay on this vile island. Half of them were already down with rheumatism. I have decided to invade Spain instead. At least the climate's better.

Yours sincerely

Julius

Lloyd's,
London
July 3, 1871

Dear Sir,

RE WRECK OF SCHOONER HESPERUS

I regret we cannot entertain your claim for the loss of the above vessel. We understand that the captain was carrying an unauthorised passenger (namely his daughter) contrary to the articles of insurance. There is evidence that just before the ship sank he tied her to the mast where her presence must have interfered with the operation of the ship, lowering of sails and so forth. Furthermore, there are indications that the captain had made a serious navigational error and was much too far north in his course.

We offer our condolences on the loss of the captain, who, we understand, froze to death.

Yours faithfully

J. Pendergast
for insurers

Canaan
April 24, 1220 BC

Dear Aaron,

I think I may be in deep trouble.

The first time I went up Mount Sinai and descended with the tablets containing the commandments of the Lord I broke them because you and some others had made a graven image, a calf I think, and I was angry. As you know I went up again and this time the Lord told me what to write and set it down myself, which I did.

With one exception.

I wrote too big at the start and although I wrote smaller and smaller as I went on I didn't have room on the tablet for everything the Lord dictated. Perhaps I should have spoken up but with all that thunder and fire and smoke going on I thought better of it. So I had to omit the last commandment. There are ten on the tablets and there should be eleven.

I could have got the last one on if number ten had been shorter, but it does go on a lot about thy neighbour's house and his menservants and his maidservants and so forth, and the frequent repetition of "Thou shalt not covet" (incidentally, I hope I spelled it right. I have an idea it might have two "t"s.) As it was, by writing very tiny I just got the last word of number ten in the corner. After that I pretended to write.

Actually, I couldn't make head or tail of the eleventh commandment anyway. Perhaps I didn't hear it right with all that thunder but it sounded like:

THOU SHALT NOT FLY

What on earth does that mean? And it went on a bit too. The full text as far as I can remember, was:

THOU SHALT NOT FLY. For flying is the Lord's, who made the sky and the fowls of the air and the habitation thereof. And he that flieth doeth that which belongs to the Lord. Therefore he shall incur my wrath. I shall command the elements that they conspire against him. I shall cause a great fog to rise up that he may not fly. And yea, he shall wait upon the elements. Three days shall he wait. And yet shall his duty be not free. And he shall beat his breast and cry, "Would that I had not flown. Would I had been content with the earth." And none shall listen to him, yea, they shall all turn their faces away from him, because he flieth.

As I can't understand what it means, perhaps it's just as well I left it out. But don't tell anyone, please.

Your old pal,

Moses

THOU SHALL NOT COVET....
P.T.O.

St Giles,
London
August 5, 1633

Dear Rector,

I must beseech you to ring the church bell less frequently. When my good wife and I took this house three months ago we little recked that the bell would ring so often and so long. The endless clangour is driving us mad. We do not know why it is ringing. We have asked for whom the bell tolls but nobody can tell us. Unless you heed my request, however, it might well toll for thee.

John Donne

Stockholm
March 3, 1983

Dear Herr Bormann,

We must ask you to stop nominating your friend Herr Rudolph Hess for a Nobel Peace Prize. The fact that he once put in a good word when Hitler wanted to shoot you is hardly sufficient; neither is the fact that they didn't actually hang him at Nuremberg but just gave a life sentence.

As requested we are sending this letter to you Poste Restante, Montevideo.

Yours faithfully,

Sven Ohmstrad
pp. Secretary

School House,
Rugby School
Nov. 3, 1823

Dear Mr Webb Ellis,

I regret I shall have to ask you to remove your son William from the school. He is a persistent cheat at games. This was first discovered during the cricket season when he dismissed a record number of opponents while keeping wicket, mostly by catches. Unfortunately, it came to light that he had secreted in his gloves a small metal device which made a clicking noise when pressed, simulating the sound of a snick. During the annual cross-country your son and a boy named East outstripped the field and were alone. Seeing he was about to be passed by East, Webb Ellis collapsed shrieking in pain. East, who is a kind-hearted lad, ran back to a cottage for help, upon which your wretched son got up and finished first. Luckily, he was incriminated by the evidence of a passing farm labourer.

However, the full depths of his depravity only came to light this football season. Early on he had to be reprimanded for tying an opponent's feet together with his own bootlaces during a long scrummage involving fifty players. On another occasion, when a kick at goal was being taken he lifted the goalpost out of the ground as the ball passed, causing the kick to miss.

But yesterday saw his most dastardly crime. Playing for the school against School House in our annual match, he found himself with the ball at his feet in front of the School House goal. Instead of trying to kick it through, the miscreant picked it up in his hands, ran between the goalposts and placed it on the ground. When I upbraided him he was insolent. "Do you call that a goal, sir?" I demanded. He replied without shame, "No, but it was a d——d good try." In all my days I have never seen such a piece of barefaced cheating. What would happen if every boy followed his example? What would become of the noble game of football? Already there are signs that other boys are copying his crime. Only this afternoon I discovered a group from the fifth form actually throwing the ball from one to another instead of kicking it. I immediately flogged them but I fear the rot has set in.

I shudder to think what will happen to your son in later life. Nothing lies ahead but obloquy and oblivion unless he reforms.

I am, sir, your most obedient servant,

Dr Thomas Arnold
Headmaster

Mafeking
Feb. 9, 1900

Dear General Kitchener,

Here is a further report on the siege, smuggled through the Boer lines by our usual route. All are in good heart and we do not think the Boers will attack for some time, but will content themselves with tightening the blockade around the town. The main difficulty is with the Boer artillery fire, which can reach almost every part of the garrison. In this respect, I have had great help from a special corps I have formed from civilians to carry messages, put out fires and so forth. Originally I raised the corps from among youngsters, but they proved unreliable, smoking and playing cards when they should have been attending their duties, so I reorganised it for men over fifty and it has been a great success. I have taken over their training personally and every one of them can now light a fire by rubbing two sticks together. I make them do this every morning. The only trouble is we are running out of sticks. Please send some with the relief column.

It has given me an idea for when the war is over and we return from South Africa. I shall form a corps of men over fifty and call them the Scouts (the name we give our Mafeking volunteers). They will wear brown uniforms and large brown hats and will train in woodcraft, lighting fires with two sticks and helping other people. The future lies with the middle-aged. Youngsters are no good at all.

Yours,

A. Baden-Powell (General)

Rochester,
Kent
Dec. 24, 1843

Dear Mr Scrooge,

I really must apologise to you for the unfortunate impression of your character which I gave in my recent book *A Christmas Carol*. I have been totally misled and deceived by the wretched Bob Cratchit, your clerk, whom I supposed a victim of misfortune. Yesterday I received a letter from The Cripplegate Charitable Fund for Distressed Clerks informing me they have discovered that Cratchit, in whom they knew I was interested, has for some years now been receiving money from six different charities at once! He tells them all the same story apparently, viz. that he has a large family, a crippled son and a rapacious employer. Of course, they have cancelled his annuity.

On receipt of this communication I immediately set out for London and called at the Cratchit house without warning, saying I had come to ask if they needed help this Christmas. To my surprise I found the crippled son Timothy, or Tiny Tim as he is called, capering about the room using his crutch to beat his fifteen-year-old sister. I asked him the reason for this unseemly behaviour and he replied. "She ate some of my caviar." Mr and Mrs Cratchit were plainly thrown into confusion by my visit and endeavoured to hide a bottle of champagne from which they had been drinking. Mrs Cratchit offered me tea without sugar, saying they could not afford such luxuries, but when she opened the cupboard to get the tea, strawberries cascaded all over the room. Robert Cratchit began to whine about how badly his employer treated him, how he had no money, etc., but at that moment there was a knock at the door and a tradesman called out, "Mr Cratchit, I have brought your Christmas goose."

Meanwhile the child Timothy tried to support his father's pose by limping heavily and crying, "God bless us all," but when his sister maliciously pinched him he cried, "———you for a d———d bitch," and chased her outside, waving his crutch at her. On returning, he pulled a bottle of gin from under the sofa, drank about a quarter of a pint, and fell asleep. Later he asked me to change a £5 note and became abusive when I could not.

As I left the house the sister approached me with a wheedling smile and said she would give me a good time for half a crown. When I declined she said, "All right, two shillings then, but don't tell my father or he will want some of the money."

I cannot tell you how distressed I am that you should have been misunderstood and your reputation sullied, even though it was all caused by Cratchit's deceit. I feel I must make amends to you somehow and I think the best way would be to introduce you into another book and vindicate your name. The most suitable would be a novel I intend to start soon called *Edwin Drood*. I. would plan to have your good self appear in the last chapter and solve the mystery of who murdered the central character.

Meanwhile, I send you every good wish for a Merry Christmas. I expect you will be spending it quietly at home as usual.

Yours sincerely,

Charles Dickens

Paris
Nov. 18, 1746

Dear Mac,

I have now settled down here after that awful battle at Culloden Moor and I want you to tell everybody to stop planning another rebellion – I have no intention of going through that again. I think it all began at Culloden when I uttered the phrase, "Gentlemen, it is time for every man to look to himself," or words to that effect. I meant it as an order for a last suicide charge against the English, but the Scottish army was so glad to retreat they ran away and I got caught in the rush and carried to the rear. As you know they smuggled me over by boat to the islands, but what you don't know is that I had to stay at the house of a filthy slut called Flora Macdonald, who fed me on nothing but porridge and whisky, both of which I loathe. She kept putting my face between her hands and saying "Mah puir wee Prince, wha' ha' the English bastards done to ye?" Once she tried to get into bed with me. The sanitation was awful, too. To crown it all, a piper played night and day a song composed in honour of my escape called "Over the Sea to Skye". They used to wake me up in the middle of the night to hear it.

France, however, is lovely – much nicer than Edinburgh, where they throw the slops from the windows into Lawnmarket. They have a thing here called a privy. Instead of whisky I drink wine, instead of porridge and haggis I eat the finest fricassées, and instead of bagpipes I listen to Bach and Handel. Please tell everyone I am glad the rebellion failed and I shall not be coming back. My advice to everyone is to swear loyalty to that old idiot King George.

Yours sincerely,

Prince Charlie ("Bonnie")

Notre Dame,
Paris
Oct. 16, 1785

Dear Archdeacon,

I would like to draw your attention to something unpleasant in the cathedral. I was passing through last night just after angelus when I was horrified to see a strange ape-like figure swinging across the nave by the chandeliers. He went out through a window and later I saw him climbing a drainpipe and cackling to himself. He appeared to be some sort of hunchback or dwarf and I nearly mistook him for a gargoyle.

Who is he? Why can't he walk about like other people? Is it really necessary for him to progress by swinging from chandeliers or climbing up pipes? We cannot have this sort of thing going on. This is a place of worship, not a zoo. Kindly instruct the verger to have this person removed. There are homes run by the blessed sisters for people like him.

It did occur to me he might be a penitent. If so, I would have thought a dozen Hail Marys would have been better. Tell Father Jacques to stop handing out ridiculous penances like swinging from the roof.

Incidentally there is a strong smell of boiling lead coming from somewhere near the roof. Please see to this as well.

The Bishop

St John's Wood,
London
August 5, 1904

Dear Peter,

I'm sorry, this is a Dear John letter. Our affair just isn't going to pan out (sorry for the awful pun, darling). I know you are a dear, sweet, little chap, but that isn't enough. A girl needs something more. Let's face it, the physical side of our relationship has been pretty disastrous. Whenever I want you to love me you just stand there fluttering your wings and saying, "Watch me fly, Wendy." This romantic stuff about killing pirates is all very well but a girl does have her emotional needs. Just occasionally she needs to be taken into a man's arms and loved, not wafted around the bloody bedroom like a moth.

The trouble is that you are still very much a child. I think this is reflected in your choice of friends. To be frank, most of them are fairies.

I hope we shall always be good friends.

Yours affectionately,

Wendy

Somewhere in the
Pacific Ocean
April 24, 1521

To His Majesty the King of Spain

Sire,

I have achieved that which you commanded and have sailed westwards from Spain to the Pacific through a narrow strait at the bottom of the Americas, which I have taken the liberty of calling The Straits of Magellan, and I am now returning to Spain by sailing onwards. But there be many perils ahead and in case I should succumb I am setting down my conclusions now. I wish it to be known that as a result of my circumnavigation I have solved the problem that has baffled mankind since the dawn of history.

The earth is square.

For many years it seemed to me foolish to think it round when there is uphill and downdale on it. The stars above do not appear to be round, but irregular in shape. And why does not all the sea run off the earth, if it is indeed a globe? Why is it not harder for my ship to travel North (or uphill) than South (or downhill)? After weighing these matters I reached my conclusion. Since I travelled no faster going South than North then I must have been sailing on the level. I concluded that the earth is a cube, full of water and I am sailing round the top. Provided I do not fall off the edge I look forward to returning to Spain with the fruits of my discovery.

Your loyal servant,

Ferdinand Magellan

New York
August 4, 1869

Sir,

Your employment with the Union Pacific Railroad is hereby terminated. As chief surveyor it was your duty to see the two sections, that working from the Pacific coast and the one working from the East, came together smoothly. And what happened? When I went last month to the ceremony to mark the final meeting of the east and west sections I discovered the people laying the westbound track were seventy-five miles north of those constructing the eastbound line. In fact the westbound party had gone past by 200 miles and were heading for the Pacific. They couldn't understand why it was getting so warm. As you know we had to put a sharp bend in the railroad so we could have the ceremony of the golden spike.

Another thing: you have been making money by selling illegal tickets to Redskins. Last week a whole party of braves in full warpaint travelled by train from Moose Horn to Skeleton Gulch, massacred another tribe, and caught the train back. The cavalry officer who captured them tells me they had special cheap party tickets. How many more times must I tell you this is a railroad, not a damned warpath?

Yours faithfully,

R. Sangster Wurtzheimer
Vice-President
Union Pacific Railroad

Jerusalem
Friday

Boys,

Inside you will find your lunch. I have packed it carefully so don't unwrap it until you need to eat it. There are seven small loaves and a few fishes. Half is for Isaac and half for Simon. It is not much for the two of you so don't go sharing it with anybody else like you usually do. Keep it to yourselves. And be home early. Leave as soon as the preacher has finished. I want you back by supper at the latest. Last time you listened to him you were gone for forty days and forty nights.

Mother

Bayswater Road Comprehensive School,
London W2
Dec. 3, 1983

Dear Mr Bunter,

There are one or two points concerning your son William which I should like to discuss now he has been here three months since the closure of Greyfriars. He is obviously finding it difficult to adapt to a State school.

Apart from his weight – which is the subject of a separate letter from the school medical officer – there is his habit of borrowing money against the arrival of a postal order at home. Since he came to us in September he has borrowed £356, all in sums of 50p, from the more gullible pupils and I must ask you to stop this immediately. I am also worried about the type of education he received at Greyfriars. He knows nothing of sociology and Afro-asian studies, merely saying, "Mr Quelch didn't teach those." His sole interest seems to be food and he regularly obtains three dinners by wheedling the dinner ladies.

Then there is the matter of his language. The whole school is imitating him and shouting things such as, "Yarooo you rotter, leggo I say." I even heard a West Indian youth call "cave" the other day. The use of these outmoded upper-class phrases is destroying everything our sociology department has been trying to achieve for fifteen years.

Lastly, please tell him we do not have corporal punishment at this school. There is no need for him to stuff an exercise book down his trousers and blubber for mercy every time I ask to see him.

Yours faithfully,

A. Trend, BA Headmaster

P.S. I think he also needs new glasses.

Florence
April 7, 1543

Dear Lady Capulet,

I cannot tell you how distressed I was to hear of the accident to your daughter but I did warn you nobody was to use the balcony for twenty-four hours. However, I do hope most sincerely that Miss Juliet recovers soon and the young man's skull heals quickly. It is lucky that a trained nurse and a friar were on hand at the time to give prompt assistance. Do not worry, I am sure she will walk again.

I think it would be better to brick up the balcony altogether. After all, your daughter will not be using it for some time and I doubt if the young man will either.

I will come to see you about it as soon as I have finished the job I am working on. I am building a tomb for Mr Mercutio.

Yours sincerely,

G. Tomasino
Builder

Page 1, 91
Lady Capulet: Mother of Juliet in Shakespeare's *Romeo and Juliet*.

Page 2
Shadrak, Meshak and Abednego, as related in the Old Testament, were thrown into a fiery furnace by King Nebuchadnezzar for refusing to worship false gods, but miraculously survived.

Page 3
A traditional story says King Alfred, hiding from the Danes, was asked to watch some cakes cook by a peasant, but let them burn.

Page 4
St Bernard's Pass: Region of the Alps, between Piedmont, Italy and Valais, Switzerland, famous for the ancient hospice near the crest which once used dogs to seek stranded travellers. Hence the St Bernard breed of mountain dog.

Page 5
King Harold was killed by an arrow in the eye at Hastings in 1066.

Page 6, 29, 39
The leaning Tower of Pisa is one of the world's best-known buildings. It started to lean almost as soon as it was finished in the Middle Ages and has constantly given difficulty ever since.

Page 8
Faustus, in Marlowe's play of that name, sold his soul to the Devil in exchange for worldly pleasures. Eventually the Devil came to claim him.

Page 9
William Tell: Swiss hero said to have been sentenced, for refusing to salute the Hapsburg badge, to shoot an apple off his son's head. He was successful.

Page 10
The Bible describes (I Samuel, 17) how the Philistines sent the giant Goliath to do single combat with an Israelite champion. He was killed by a shepherd boy called David with a stone from his sling.

Page 11
Tradition says that when Queen Elizabeth was about to step into a nasty puddle, Sir Walter Raleigh threw down his expensive cloak over it.

Page 12
Grimaldi: The world's most famous clown, who did not properly develop his comic talent until he left Drury Lane after a quarrel.

Page 13
"Was this the face that launched a thousand ships?" Christopher Marlowe's description of Helen of Troy in *Faustus*.

Page 14
The mutiny on HMS *Bounty* is one of the world's most famous sea dramas, filmed several times. It arose from a conflict between Capt. Bligh and a midshipman, Fletcher Christian, over Bligh's brutal discipline.

Page 15
Marconi sent the first transatlantic radio message from Newfoundland to Cornwall.

Page 16
In *The Picture of Dorian Grey* by Oscar Wilde, the hero sells his soul to the Devil on condition that he always remains youthful. He does so, but instead his portrait ages and reflects his crimes.

Page 17
Genghis Khan was a peasant's son who conquered most of Asia. Eventually his empire stretched from the China Sea to the Caspian Sea.

Page 18
King Robert Bruce, of Scotland, while hiding from the English, watched a spider struggling to climb up its web and is said to have been inspired to "try, try again", and this time was successful in his fight for Scotland.

Page 20
Richard I (Coeur-de-Lion, or Lionheart) was captured by the Duke of Austria while returning from the Crusades. His minstrel Blondel toured Europe to find him, singing his favourite song (which they had composed together) outside every likely castle. Eventually he discovered Richard and arranged ransom.

Page 21
Queen Cleopatra was famous for bathing in asses' milk.

Page 22
The Bible (Daniel, chapter 5) describes the story of The Writing on the Wall, when Belshazzar held a feast and during it a ghostly hand wrote mysterious words on the wall. No one could tell what the message meant until they asked Daniel, who interpreted. Belshazzar died next night.

Page 24
Gray's poem *Elegy in a Country Churchyard* was written in the churchyard at Stoke Poges, Bucks. Later he was buried there.

Page 26
Nelson, the famous English naval commander, when ordered to withdraw on the approach of enemy ships, put his telescope to his blind eye and said, "I see no ships."

Page 27
In Shaw's *Pygmalion* (perhaps better known by the musical version *My Fair Lady*), a cockney girl called Eliza Doolittle is taught to speak and behave like an upper-class woman by Professor Higgins as a social experiment.

Page 28
Sir Isaac Newton is said to have formulated the law of gravity after seeing an apple fall from a tree.

Page 30
Marshal Foch: "My centre is giving way, my right is in retreat. Situation excellent; I shall attack!"

Page 31
Sir Francis Drake was playing bowls on Plymouth Hoe when a messenger told him the Spanish Armada was in sight. He is reputed to have said, "We have time to finish our game."

Page 32
The Duke of Clarence was drowned in a butt of malmsey in the Tower of London on the orders of Richard III.

Page 33
The Sphinx: Ancient monument near Cairo famous for its enigmatic smile.

Page 35
"I shall return" – Gen. MacArthur on being forced out of Bataan by Japanese troops in World War Two. He did.

Page 36
Spurius and Herminius, despite their names, held the bridge with Horatius at Rome in the classic battle, to give time for its destruction so the foe might not cross. They ran back as it collapsed but Horatius, as narrated in Macaulay's famous poem, had to swim.

Page 38
The *Titanic*, the world's newest and biggest ocean liner, sank on her maiden voyage to New York in 1912, after striking an iceberg.

Page 40
Ophelia's burial in *Hamlet* is preceded by a famous comic scene between two gravediggers, in which Yorick's skull is tossed about. "Alas, poor Yorick . . ."

Page 42
Dr Watson was the faithful biographer of the great detective Sherlock Holmes, in the stories by A. Conan Doyle.

Page 46
Madame Defarge: Character in Dickens' book *A Tale of Two Cities*. She knitted at the foot of the guillotine while executions were carried out.

Page 48

Hiawatha was the hero of Longfellow's famous poem about Indians. It is notable for its unusual metre, imitated here.

Page 51

King Arthur, when dying, told Sir Bedivere to throw his immortal sword Excalibur into a lake. Twice he disobeyed but the third time threw it in and an arm "clothed in white samite, mystical" came out, caught it and disappeared back into the lake.

Page 52

In Xanadu did Kubla Khan
A stately pleasure dome decree;
Where Alph, the sacred river, ran
Through caverns measureless to man
Down to a sunless sea.

– Samuel Taylor Coleridge.

Page 53

The Pilgrim Fathers sailed in *The Mayflower* from Plymouth in 1620 to found the first colony in New England. A large number of them were Puritans fleeing from religious persecution.

Page 54

The ceiling of the Sistine Chapel in Rome, painted by Michelangelo, is one of his greatest works.

Page 55

Job: Biblical character tested by God with terrible tribulations which he bore with patience.

Page 58

Penicillin is reputed to have been discovered accidentally when Sir Alexander Fleming found some germ cultures had been destroyed by a mould.

Page 59

In Stevenson's *Treasure Island*, Long John Silver, the pirate chief, had a parrot which constantly repeated, "Pieces of eight."

Page 60

The *Mary Rose* sank suddenly and mysteriously just outside Portsmouth Harbour, in full view of Henry VIII, while sailing to fight the French.

Page 61

Legend tells of the little Dutch boy who saved a flood by sticking his thumb in a dyke. He is usually held up as an example of courage and resource.

Page 62

When Lot was fleeing from Sodom and Gomorrah in the biblical story, God forbade him to look back. His wife did so and was turned into a pillar of salt.

Page 64

"You can't make silk purses out of sows' ears" – a common saying meaning that some things are incapable of being improved.

Page 68

One of Andrew Marvell's best-known poems is *To My Coy Mistress*, in which he urges his mistress to let him make love to her before it is too late. "The grave's a kind and private place / But none, I think do there embrace."

Page 69

Davy Crockett, American frontiersman, was famous for his coonskin hat with a tail hanging down.

Page 70

The town of Hamelin in Germany was immortalised by Robert Browning in his poem "The Pied Piper of Hamelin," about a strange piper who rid the town of rats and then, when his fee was disputed, led all the children away.

Page 71

Julius Caesar made a preliminary landing in England in 55 BC but sailed away.

Page 72

"It was the schooner Hesperus / That sailed the wintry sea / And the skipper had taken his little daughter, / To bear him company" – Longfellow.

Page 73

Moses wrote the Ten Commandments on Mount Sinai as the Lord spoke.

Page 76

John Donne: "Any man's death diminishes me, because I am involved in Mankind; and therefore never send to know for whom the bell tolls; it tolls for thee." This quotation inspired the title of Hemingway's novel *For Whom the Bell Tolls*.

Page 77

Last of the Nazi leaders, Rudolph Hess is still imprisoned in Berlin. Martin Bormann, Hitler's right-hand man, vanished in 1945 and was once rumoured to be in South America.

Page 78

William Webb Ellis is traditionally the founder of Rugby football. During a game of football at Rugby School in 1823 he picked up the ball and ran over the line "thus originating the distinctive feature of the modern game" as the plaque to his memory says. His grave in Menton, France, is a place of pilgrimage for rugby fans.

Page 80
General Baden-Powell, founder of the Boy Scouts, is said to have been inspired for the idea by a corps of boy messengers he enlisted during the siege of Mafeking in the Boer War.

Page 81
Bob Cratchit is the downtrodden clerk employed by Scrooge in Dickens' story *A Christmas Carol*. Dickens died before completing *Edwin Drood*.

Page 83
Bonnie Prince Charlie was forced to flee after his defeat by the English at Culloden and was saved by a Highland lass called Flora Macdonald, who disguised him as her maid and escorted him to safety.

Page 84
The Hunchback of Notre Dame was one of Charles Laughton's greatest film roles. He spent most of the film swinging around the cathedral, leering, until finally he poured molten lead from the roof on to the baddies.

Page 85
Wendy was the little girl who befriended the fairy Peter Pan in the play by James Barrie.

Page 86
Ferdinand Magellan led an expedition which was the first ever to sail round the world. But he was killed in the Phillipines.

Page 88

A golden spike was used to mark the junction of the two halves of the Union Pacific Railroad in the USA, the eastbound and the westbound sections.

Page 89

One of Christ's best-known miracles was the feeding of five thousand people who had come to hear Him with seven loaves and a few fishes collected from the crowd (Matthew 15: 34).

Page 90

Billy Bunter was the fat, comic schoolboy who was the centre of Frank Richards' famous stories of public school life in the *Magnet* comic in the thirties and forties.

BACHELOR BOYS

THE YOUNG ONES' BOOK

BEN ELTON · LISE MAYER · RIK MAYALL

Call it bad karma or anarchy in the U.K., there's never been anything quite like the cult-hit T.V. series *The Young Ones* – totally bizarre, totally original, totally aggressive and . . . totally TOTAL. So, here are the Young Ones in their own write at last: Rick the Radical Poet, Vyvyan the Psychopathic Punk, Neil the Suicidal Hippy, and Mike, the Would-Be Spiv. Together they reveal The Ultimate Truth About Everything to their avid fans, including absolutely zillions of helpless hints on:

★ HOBBIES
Neil's 101 really interesting things to do with a tea-cup
★ FILTH
Some kissing hints from Vyvyan. Lesson one: Snog the Dog
★ LAUGHS
Including Rick's only joke: These are my pants and I'm sticking to them!!!
PLUS
a controversial statement from the Acne Liberation Front. The Young Ones say: WEAR YOUR SPOTS WITH PRIDE

NON-FICTION/HUMOUR 0 7221 5765 7 £2.95

EVERYTHING YOU NEED TO KNOW ABOUT SPORT (AND A LOT OF THINGS YOU DON'T)!

The Book Of SPORTS LISTS

CRAIG AND DAVID BROWN

Who 'floats like a butterfly and stings like one too'? Who gave up sex for a year in order to improve his game – and what does it cost to persuade John McEnroe to play with your racquets for a year? Which sportsman said 'I'd give my right arm to be a pianist' – and what do Torvill and Dean have to say about each other?

THE BOOK OF SPORTS LISTS brings together the most remarkable things ever done and the funniest things ever said in the name of sport around the world. Record-breakers and blunderers, prudes and Casanovas, good sports and bad sports, they're all in THE BOOK OF SPORTS LISTS.

NON-FICTION/HUMOUR/SPORT 0 7221 1935 6 £2.50

Don't miss Craig Brown and Lesley Cunliffe's THE BOOK OF ROYAL LISTS, also available in Sphere Books.

The HYPOCHONDRIAC'S HANDBOOK

DR. LEE SCHREINER

DR. GEORGE THOMAS

The Health Service prides itself on its ability to care for the sick – but what provision is there for the misunderstood minority, the hypochondriacs? Unfairly discriminated against by the entire medical profession, they are continually denied the attention they so obviously *deserve* . . .

At long last, THE HYPOCHONDRIAC'S HANDBOOK redresses the balance. An invaluable aid to all sufferers from imaginary illnesses, it tells of a host of alarming and hideous ailments which may befall the permanent malingerer at any time, plus how to fake symptoms when the disease is not actually contracted. You'll never feel safe again, once you've discovered which Life Threatening Infections You Can Catch From Your Pets . . . how Physical Fitness is Hazardous to Your Health . . . How to Recognise Your Own Psychiatric Emergencies . . . and The Hypochondriac's Guide to Sexual Dysfunctions!

HUMOUR 0 7221 7720 8 £1.50